Animal Alphabet

Written by Mary Hogan   Illustrated by Consuelo Udave

McGraw-Hill
School Division

New York   Farmington

1

Aa

Albert is **acting**.

Bonnie is **b**atting.

Cc

Carla is cutting.

4

Donna is **d**ancing.

Ed is **e**xploring.

Ff

Fern is fishing.

Gus is **g**ardening.

9

Hh

Hannah is **hammering**.

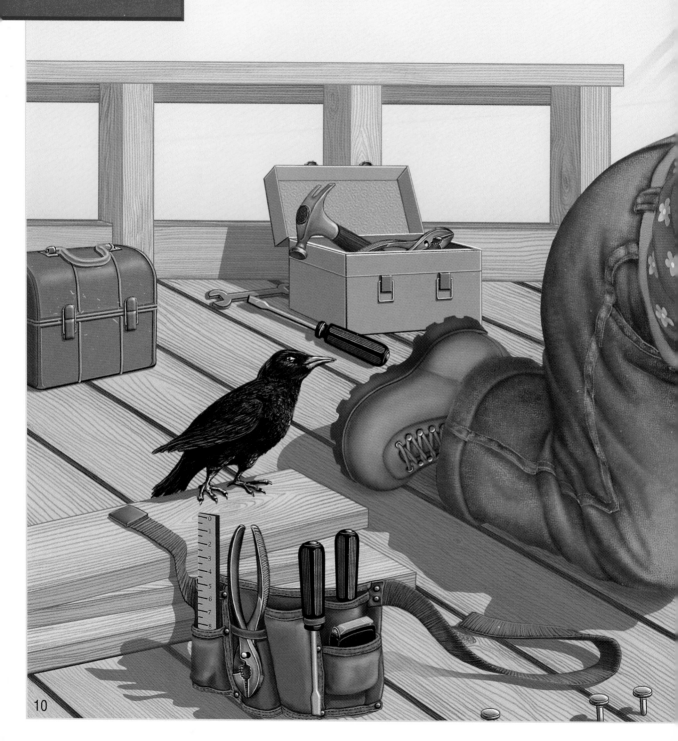

I i

Iggy is inventing.

Jack is **juggling**.

13

Kara is kicking.

Ll

Leo is looking.

Mark is **m**ixing.

Nn

Nell is **napping**.

Oscar is **o**perating.

Pp

Pat is pumping.

Queenie is **quivering**.

Rr

Ron is **r**unning.

Ss

Sally is **s**inging.

Alexa is X-raying.

Yy

Yancy is **y**elling.

Zelda is **z**ipping.

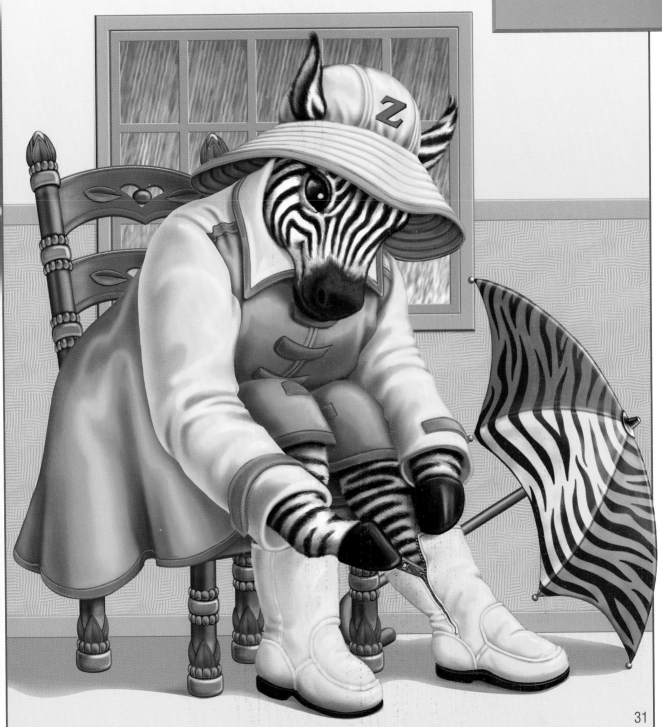

31

Alphabet Animals Pictured in This Book

Aa	alligator		Nn	nightingale
Bb	bear		Oo	otter
Cc	cat		Pp	pig
Dd	dinosaur		Qq	quail
Ee	elephant		Rr	raccoon
Ff	ferret		Ss	seal
Gg	gorilla		Tt	turtle
Hh	hippopotamus		Uu	umbrella bird
Ii	iguana		Vv	vicuña
Jj	jaguar		Ww	walrus
Kk	kangaroo		Xx	fox
Ll	lion		Yy	yak
Mm	monkey		Zz	zebra